THE MAGIC PILL

A Mental Health Companion for the Gastric Bypass Patient

By Teri Kai Holtzclaw, Ph.D.

THE MAGIC PILL A Mental Health Companion for the Gastric Bypass
Patient

Copyright © 2001 by Teri Kai Holtzclaw, Ph.D.
First Edition
All right reserved. This book, or parts thereof, may not be
reproduced in any form without permission.
ISBN: 0-9712601-1-7
Library of Congress Cataloging-in-Publication Data
Library of Congress Control Number: 2001127205
Holtzclaw, Teri Kai.
THE MAGIC PILL
A Mental Health Companion for the Gastric Bypass Patient
Teri Kai Holtzclaw.

Cover Photography
Copyright © 1997 by Morris Press

Printed in the United States by Morris Publishing
3212 East Highway 30 • Kearney, NE 68847
1-800-650-7888

THE MAGIC PILL A Mental Health Companion for the Gastric Bypass
Patient

To Sandy:
You continue to be my source of strength and sanity.

To Harley & Cleo:
Thank you for your unconditional love and companionship.

By, Teri Kai Holtzclaw, Ph.D.   3

THE MAGIC PILL A Mental Health Companion for the Gastric Bypass
Patient

By, Teri Kai Holtzclaw, Ph.D.   **4**

THE MAGIC PILL A Mental Health Companion for the Gastric Bypass
Patient

When we choose to love ourselves. We choose to love not only our brains, but our bodies too. When we invest, believe and buy in, to personal integrity - We help others on the planet choose to do the same...by our example.

By, Teri Kai Holtzclaw, Ph.D.   5

THE MAGIC PILL A Mental Health Companion for the Gastric Bypass Patient

By, Teri Kai Holtzclaw, Ph.D.   6

THE MAGIC PILL A Mental Health Companion for the Gastric Bypass
Patient

Table of Contents

By, Teri Kai Holtzclaw, Ph.D.   **7**

THE MAGIC PILL A Mental Health Companion for the Gastric Bypass
Patient

By, Teri Kai Holtzclaw, Ph.D.   **8**

Acknowledgements

My thanks and love to all those people who have lent their support and contributed directly and/or indirectly in the adventures and insights shared in this book. Words can barely express the impact on my life and on the pages of this book by Dr. Edward Waits, Nancy Waits and Karen Bonney, who have championed a "top notch" Bariatric program and lavishly supported me with their love, friendship and tireless energy. Much thanks to our beautiful cat Cleo for her endless patience and companionship while I worked on this manuscript. And to our precious puppy Harley for teaching me that I could throw a tennis ball and type simultaneously. If a book could be said to have an ultimate power behind it, this one had my life partner, Sandy, who touched every page with her unconditional love and keen sense of understanding. She continues to inspire me to succeed. All of these people and pets have been gifts in my life. I feel honored to have their support and grateful for what I have learned from each of them.

.

THE MAGIC PILL A Mental Health Companion for the Gastric Bypass
Patient

By, Teri Kai Holtzclaw, Ph.D.   10

INTRODUCTION

The causes and solutions to the problems posed by obesity are uniquely addressed in THE MAGIC PILL, not unlike it's predecessor This is NOT Brain Surgery! One of the things that set Dr. Holtzclaw's books apart from others on obesity is the fact that they specifically confront weight loss maintenance after weight loss surgery.

Her books give you strategies for realistically thinking ahead, thinking preventatively and having a sense of purpose that can help you deal with weight loss success issues. They deal with the interpretation of life, how you think, what you think and how you can handle guilt and responsibility when dealing with weight issues. This is NOT Brain Surgery! was a primer to this greater and more in depth book THE MAGIC PILL The focus in her first book was to introduce us to the idea of walking this earth with personal integrity and trusting that we can be honest, if only with ourselves. This book takes us further into the journey of self-discovery and explores integrity issues coupled with responsibility and personal choice. All of Dr. Holtzclaw's philosophies stem from what she calls Universal Truths. That personal integrity, happiness and peace of mind DO affect our weight loss maintenance success.

And that these genuine truths are instilled within each and every one of us.

Dr. Holtzclaw has said, "We are all working from what we've learned we know to be true. And then, we spend a lifetime revising our knowledge, and our definition of Truth, to compensate for what we really know and learn as conscious human beings." Overall, the usefulness of these books is found in being able to place the various aspects of weight loss into the framework of the rest of your life. This book, THE MAGIC PILL, helps you to understand the nature of weight gain and weight loss. It helps you see weight loss as more than just a physical problem - it involves your cognitive senses as well. It's an integrated event.

THE MAGIC PILL A Mental Health Companion for the Gastric Bypass Patient

Before Weight Loss Surgery 1996

After Weight Loss Surgery 2001

By, Teri Kai Holtzclaw, Ph.D.

<u>THE MAGIC PILL</u> A Mental Health Companion for the Gastric Bypass
Patient

By, Teri Kai Holtzclaw, Ph.D.   **14**

THE MAGIC PILL A Mental Health Companion for the Gastric Bypass Patient

PERSONAL NOTE

Like many obese people, I lived with my everyday fears, anger, anxiety, impatience and distrust about weight loss. Somehow, simultaneously, I searched for a philosophy, psychology or spiritual connection, which might enable me to make sense out of my eating disorder and resolve the disappointment and dissatisfaction that haunted me. The energizing and sometimes exhausting journey through books, religion, twelve step programs, workshops, philosophy and psychology courses yielded some answers, but never "the answer." Finally, I returned to the basic truths of humankind. I decided to practice the art of "gratitude" and indulge myself in mastering personal integrity. I embraced happiness for the sake of being happy and released fear for the sake of being afraid. I no longer played a passive role in my life. Personal responsibility became my goal. It was exciting and challenging to reclaim what I never thought I had -My inner peace. My pursuit of basic truths empowered me more than I had ever anticipated. My journey through obesity, weight loss surgery and self-realization has been the most empowering and enriching experience of my life. I am honored to be where I am and who I am, doing what I love, and sharing my journey with you. It is my hope that as you read this book, you too, will discover the power behind living basic human truths. Choose to find peace within.... Love your body...it is not a vessel. It permeates genetic memory throughout every living cell.

By, Teri Kai Holtzclaw, Ph.D.   **15**

You ARE your body.   This is only the beginning.   Stay with
me...you ARE not alone.

THE MAGIC PILL A Mental Health Companion for the Gastric Bypass
Patient

PART I

By, Teri Kai Holtzclaw, Ph.D.   **17**

LIFE

You could reverse my surgery today and I am convinced I will be able to maintain my weight loss successfully! That's a wonderful feeling. I have spent years after having gastric bypass surgery, worrying over the possibility of the worst occurring ...having a complication and having to have my surgery revised.

I told myself that without gastric bypass surgery I could not maintain the healthy eating habits that I have developed over the past five years. I told myself that I wouldn't keep exercising and maintaining an active professional and social life. Somehow, I managed to place all the power and all the credit on the surgical procedure itself. Denying myself any of the accolades for the hard work and effort. Including the mental changes and the lifestyle changes I have had to make to be successful. I wanted to write a book focusing on the changes I made that brought me to this realization. It's important that I establish early on that I did not believe I could successfully maintain weight loss without maintaining this surgical intervention. I thought that the surgery alone had "cured" me of my eating disorder. I also thought that losing the surgery would "kill" the new and improved me that had emerged from three hundred plus pounds. I was wrong. Not only is reversing the surgical procedure unwise, but there is no turning back from the mental and spiritual transformation either. Gastric bypass surgery was the jump-start I needed to get off in the right direction. Once, "energized" or "motivated" if you will, by the surgery, I was then able to take on the long-term goals of eating right and exercise. Gastric bypass surgery is not the alternative to living and eating well. Gastric bypass surgery is the tool in which one can embrace short-term weight loss success. This surgery gave me the opportunity to envision what long term weight loss maintenance could be. This surgery did not guarantee me long term weight loss success without exercise and eating right. I am not exempt from eating smart. Anyone who has had gastric bypass surgery can tell you the benefits of caring for your physical health and the consequences of vitamin deficiencies and malnutrition if you choose not too.

THE MAGIC PILL

Many of my readers are seeking that "magic pill" to shed their pounds for them and promise them eternal thinness. The "magic pill" does not come in book form. This book will not solve your weight loss issues FOR you. It will, however, assist you in your voyage towards successful weight loss maintenance. It is designed to plant seeds of motivation and positive reinforcement of healthy eating behaviors. It can function as a "signal" telling you when you are choosing to eat to FILL or to FEEL. May I suggest approaching this book and it's contents as a friend and not as a competitor. This book has no power. The ideas and messages

remain universal to all truths. I am not saying anything new or
creating any of these solutions out of "thin" air. I am merely, re-
packaging, re-designing and reinventing what humankind has
known since the beginning. There is no magic pill. There is only
this life. And IT, alone, is magical. Embrace your decision to
change. If you can't change you - Who can? If "change" seems
like it is larger than life and you think it is larger than your ability to
handle it. Try handing over the power to something or someone
greater then you. Once your Higher Power has a hold of what you
believe is out of your capabilities to handle. It's time to "act" as if
you can handle it. It's time to "trust" the abilities you do own and
know that whatever life brings to you is yours. If you are stuck in
what I call "career confusion" and you can't break free of using the
phrase "I don't understand" whenever a discussion about honesty
and denial comes up. If you are working off of childhood
perceptions ingrained in your mental programming and no longer
can recall why you say and do what you say and do. If you are
taking baby steps one minute and wind sprinting through life the
next minute and you're not sure what direction you're heading. If
you use food to avoid confrontation in every relationship in your
life. If any or all of these describe your experience, this book is for
you.

DENIAL

The topic of denial is complex and full of winding paths that all lead back to one universal truth: Be honest with yourself and the rest will follow. I realize those of us who are drowning in denial will look at that statement and wonder why I wrote it. After all, "we are honest." I am not speaking of being honest with others or in your daily interaction with the external world. I am speaking of personal integrity. Being truly honest with yourself and being accountable to yourself only. I am speaking of the honest voice within. The voice that tells you how you truly feel just before you silence her or him. Silencing what you know with what you've been taught or told you should be thinking or feeling instead. That inner voice is you. The voice that will not stop and continues to call out for your approval, love and acceptance IS you. We all experience internal dialogues with ourselves on a conscious and unconscious level twenty-fours a day seven days a week. Even in our sleep, we are communicating thoughts and feelings through our dreams and different states of unconsciousness. We are amazing creations!

STATE OF PERFECT

Many obese persons suffer from striving to be perfect. This impossible aspiration creates continuous disappointment and self-loathing. We set ourselves up for failure when we set such unrealistic goals for ourselves. For some of us, it starts out quite innocently. As children, we placed a parent or perhaps both parents on a pedestal. We admired and deified our mothers and or our fathers. We watched as they sacrificed their happiness for our own. Many of us felt anger, resentment and rage. The mixed internal dialogue going on in our brains and our hearts confused us. On one hand, we knew we felt anger resentment and rage. On the other hand, we knew that we "should" feel gratitude appreciation and respect for the sacrifices made on our behalf. The anger stemmed from the longing to see our parents happy. We couldn't make them choose personal happiness, so we did what we could - We chose to fulfill their happiness for them. We resented having to sacrifice our lives and our hopes to live out the lives they sacrificed for us. And the wheel turns. When will it stop? It stops when we choose to forgive our parents for being human. It stops when we choose to forgive ourselves for being less then perfect. It stops when we acknowledge the voice within us as the truth.

By, Teri Kai Holtzclaw, Ph.D.   22

It stops when we recognize that the other voices are simply a product of years of constant negative programming from outside sources.

It stops when you decide to choose happiness. It stops when you give up the Norman Rockwell fantasy and live out the journey that is uniquely yours.

Who Comes First

Most of us have many demands placed on our time and energy. Spouse, children, spiritual or community groups are important and make living worthwhile, but can make finding time for one's self a challenge. Balancing the time you spend on others with personal time for yourself can help you become happier and more productive.

Me

Take a moment to think about how well you take care of yourself--both physically and emotionally. Do you eat three moderate meals a day? Do you exercise each week, and get a check-up once a year? Answering yes to these questions means that you take care of your body.

Now think about your emotional well-being. Do you regularly set
aside "quiet" time for yourself, meditating, writing, and thinking or
praying? Do you make time regularly to enjoy nature or other quiet,
restful places? All these activities can help you recover from life's
stresses.

You

Reaching outside you can give your life great meaning and joy.
Reaching out means sharing with others--your family co-workers,
friends, and a non-profit organization--virtually everything that's
not you! Sharing with others takes time and energy, but the rewards
are worth the effort. Your self-esteem and sense of purpose in life
increase when you share a common goal or bond with others.

Balance is Essential to Healthy Living

Reaching out to others all the time would leave you exhausted.
Living only for yourself would leave you lonely and empty. Finding
the balance between the two is the key to a rich and contented life.
To find your personal balance, look at how you spend your time
and energy. Write down your main activities each day for a week or
two. Then add up the hours spent "for me" and "for others." You
might realize that you would like to give more to others, or take
more time for yourself.

When you are creating balance for yourself, you need to decide what is most important to you.

Going with the Flow

Finding your balance is a day-by-day matter. If you are able to change as your life circumstances change, caring for yourself and others will make your life healthy and satisfying.

FOOD IS NOT FUEL AND I AM NOT A MACHINE

Food is NOT just "fuel" for our bodies. We ARE NOT machines to be oiled or maintained. We require more than just "fuel" to run on. We are Physical, mental and spiritual beings. We are whole. Maintaining physical fitness is one part of our whole -It is not the sum total of who we are. Whoever said we should look at food as merely "fuel" for our physical bodies did not consider the consequences of their words.

I have said it before. Food acts as" glue" that binds families, cultures, and yes, even nations together. Food represents "peace" and positive "expression" of good will. Food is more than just fuel. Our society has made it so.

How sad to see ourselves -The incredible unique beings that we are as simply machines to be fueled. What a shameful message we are sending to our bodies when we say that we are only physical vehicles housing our organs. We know that every cell in our bodies contain a genetic fingerprint of who we are, where we came from and perhaps some pattern of where we are going. The mind, the body and the spirit are interconnected -threads woven through every cell and tissue within us. We act as living miracles. Not as mechanized beings needing to be fueled, but as living miracles needing to be nurtured and loved. I am deeply moved by those who come to me stating that they want to see food as nothing but a "necessary" evil. Food is something to be reckoned with three times a day. A battle to be won or for most of us suffering from eating disorders - A battle to walk away from feeling defeated yet again. My first challenge is to redirect this client's thinking process from a negative approach to a positive affirmation. Food is not the enemy. Food is and can remain a wonderful part of human existence. All things in moderation. Eating, balanced and healthy foods can be an enjoyable and guilt-free experience. Relating to food is a lot like relating to people. Not all food groups are healthy for us to eat all of the time, and not all people are healthy for us to spend time with all of the time. Some people are fun to be around some of the time. Some foods are okay to indulge yourself in some of the time. Too much of someone and some food can be destructive. When we are able to balance our smart eating choices with our everyday lives, we soon realize that it's not so much what we eat as it is why we eat. Portion size is key only for those of us who are unable to differentiate between eating to "fill up" and

eating to "feel something." We'll discuss this connection later in
the book.

SENDING MIXED MESSAGES

I am often accused of sending "mixed messages." It's true.
Therapy often imitates real life. And not unlike reality, there is no
"black and white" and there is no absolute "right and wrong." Our
eating choices are usually based on these factors: where we are,
who we are with, what we are feeling, what we can afford, and
impulsively, what we think we desire to satisfy our want - disguised
as "hunger." It is "okay" to eat what you want. As long as what
you want is healthy. Change your focus. Want foods that are good
for you and strengthen your body. Want foods that help you
maintain the successful weight loss that you worked so hard to
obtain through gastric bypass surgery. We had the surgery so that
we could "fit in" and be "normal." We didn't have weight loss
surgery so we could deprive ourselves of normal healthy food
experiences. Food is not the enemy. Everything in moderation.
Balance is key. Choose to eat well and exercise in order to
maintain a healthy lifestyle. These are all phrases that meant
nothing to us before gastric bypass surgery. Now, we have the tool
that makes accomplishing these tasks possible. Many postoperative
patients are learning that the window of opportunity to take
advantage of this newfound tool is limited. You can out eat your

surgery. You can regain the weight lost and sabotage the success earned. You see, we are not machines. A surgeon can go into our bodies and make wonderful mechanical adjustments to our stomachs, but they do not adjust our brains. This is not brain surgery! You don't wake up after decades of overeating and "think" that you're no longer hungry. Your mind has developed a habit of eating to maintain your balance, not sustain your life. This is not just science. Human life consists of mind body and spirit. Every cell in your body is genetically programmed to interconnect to every other cell. You are the sum of all your parts.

We, as a society, tend to identify each other, and ourselves, by specific parts instead of seeing one another as a whole being. One example of this "fragmented" way of thinking is the way we process our own self-worth. I am often confronted with the notion that being overweight is not a mental health issue. This proclamation is usually followed with a passionate disclosure of one's eating choices being entirely separate from their cognitive ability. Being overweight IS a product of an imbalance in our lives. The physical Imbalance is reflected in our inability to run far, walk upstairs and in some instances, sit comfortably. The imbalance is reflected in our social lives by our inability to participate in many team sports and action oriented entertainment, such as amusement park rides. The imbalance spills over into our personal and professional relationships; once again, acknowledging that our society has trained us to see one another in "fragments" (i.e., our size, and not as "whole" beings.) The process continues until every facet of who we are is affected by this imbalance. It is important to note that any imbalance in our lives is interconnected to every part of who we are. We are the "sum of our parts." I do not have to tell you how many times each day decisions are made based on your size. You make these decisions when you plan activities. Your employer and Company make decisions based on your representation of their business. It is without merit to defend our engrained behavior without acknowledging that it exists. Right or wrong is not relevant in this discussion. Reality dictates that we see others and ourselves through a very limited and narrow vision. We have the opportunity to live physically and mentally balanced lives. Our physical health is not always poor just because we choose not to exercise. But, if we do take the time and energy to tone our bodies and increase our stamina, we will have better physical health than if we didn't. Our mental health works in the same fashion. Choosing not to address your mental health does not make you mentally unstable. But, if you do choose to exercise your self awareness and pay greater attention to the "sum of all your parts" instead of focusing on only a few, you will benefit by having better mental health than if you didn't.

The Unthinkable

The emphasis on rational thought in our culture is epitomized in the
great Philosopher's words: " I think, therefore I exist."
Unfortunately, this phrase encourages us to equate our identities
with our rational minds - rather than with our entire body. There is
a negative effect with the division between our minds and our
bodies that is felt throughout our lives. Retreating into our minds,
we have forgotten how to "think" with our bodies, and how to use
them as tools of knowing. This "disconnect" is reflected in our
culture's inability to cooperate with nature and is only a larger
picture of our own inability to cooperate with our whole body. In
the mainstream of our society we have overemphasized rational
knowledge and neglected intuitive wisdom.
It is in my professional opinion that the majority of my clients are
expert rational thinkers.   Clients walk in to my office baffled by
their inability to "think" their way out of their eating disorders and
weight issues. I am required to teach them to do the Unthinkable."
It begins with an explanation of how excessive self -assertion
manifests itself as power, control, and domination of others by
force.   These are indeed the patterns prevalent in our society.
Aggressive, competitive behavior alone would make life impossible.
Balance is a constant theme in my sessions for this very reason.
Even the most ambitious, goal oriented individuals need
sympathetic support, human contact and times of spontaneity and

relaxation.   These qualities initiate a healing process that is
necessary to our weight loss maintenance and long-term success.
Unfortunately, in our culture, we value and reward only the
intellectual part of ourselves and we have discarded the intuitive
aspects.

Stop thinking with your head and start exploring your own intuitive
wisdom that manifests through your heart and communicates
through each cell in your body. You have ignored your body when
it has told you it is no longer hungry. You have ignored your body
when it has told you it IS hungry. You may have ignored your
spirit who has starved for love, your soul who starves for physical
contact and your mind who starves for understanding. You have
practiced ignoring so many parts of yourself "thinking" your way
out of every feeling that you no longer trust any connection
between your rational thoughts and your physical body. This is the
task set before me.   Not to teach a client how to advance their
intellect or "outsmart" their own intelligence. My task is to teach
"The   Unthinkable."

THE MAGIC PILL A Mental Health Companion for the Gastric Bypass
Patient

THE MAGIC PILL A Mental Health Companion for the Gastric Bypass
Patient

PART II

LESSONS

All or Nothing

If you are a card-holding member of the "all or nothing" club where
everything in life is black or white. Right or wrong. Good or bad.
Fat or thin. You, my dear reader, are in for a wonderful and
pleasurable awakening. Life is full of colors and contrasts that are
in a constant state of "whirling and swirling" around us. Imagine
for a moment what your life would be like today, if you existed in a
perfect world as a perfect being. Perhaps, the concept makes you
laugh. After all, what would be the purpose? Perhaps, you are
frightened and feel I have treaded some forbidden path by
suggesting such a thing. I am pointing out to you that living a
perfectly balanced existence is living in perfect harmony with
yourself and those around you. It is a fine line between balance and
existing as a perfect being. No one is perfect. To maintain balance
in our lives perfectly is impossible. I want you to focus on doing
what you can when you can and how you can. The rules of society
do not apply here. This space is reserved for the "experience" of
life. Life involves various degrees of negative and positive
experiences. Many decisions we make are far from perfect. Think
of the many wrong turns you have taken in your life that have
brought you to who you are today. Life is not fair. Justice does

not always prevail. We are not above being singled out and
mistreated by society for any number of reasons. I want to help
you see that life is full of contradictions. It's not what you eat that
counts so much as why you eat. And it's not so much why you eat,
as it is how much you eat. And the solution is not to get thin to be
happy. The solution lies in getting happy to be healthy. I recently
heard someone say, "happiness comes in moments and is not a state
of mind." I respectfully disagree. I believe happiness is not only a
state of mind but also a state of living. If you are experiencing
happiness in "moments," it is because you have limited your
perception of what happiness is. This book will challenge your
current definitions and perceptions of honesty, happiness and
weight loss.

If you find you are unable to experience happiness because you
choose to define happiness in unrealistic terms then you are setting
yourself up to be miserable and unhappy for the rest of your life.
Happiness, honesty and weight loss are all common experiences
that require a healthy balance of good and bad choices. It is in our
imperfection as human beings that we are able to satisfy the balance
of nature and find peace of mind. And it is within that peaceful
state of thinking and being that we find true happiness. Why are
you struggling to maintain successful weight loss after surgery?
Why has becoming thin not completed your picture frame world of
perfection? Why are you thinking about food in pounds instead of
in relationship to other parts of your life? Are you happy? What

does happiness have to do with weight loss? I intend to show you over and over in the pages of this book that happiness is, indeed, a key element in maintaining weight loss.

I Deserve This!

How many times have you "survived" another day just to sit down in front of a meal and tell yourself: "I know I shouldn't eat this, BUT: I Deserve This!" Quickly, you rationalize -even justify - ALL the reasons why you deserve to eat as much of and ALL of the food in front of you. You remind yourself that it's okay to be "human" and talk yourself through the healthiest part of you trying to STOP you. A few bites and the voice of reason has been silenced there is nothing reasonable about choosing to eat too much food and sabotaging your surgery. No one DESERVES to sabotage his or her surgery. It wasn't easy making the choice to have weight loss surgery and it wasn't easy to lose the weight you have lost up to this point. You don't DESERVE to gain back all the weight you worked so hard to lose. The next time you tell yourself you "Deserve This!" make sure you're nowhere near food. If it's a reward you're seeking for a job well done or a day well spent, seek your reward elsewhere. Get a massage; go for a walk; treat yourself to a good book or some solitude in your backyard. A reward is not always tangible. The best reward anyone can give himself or herself is simply to acknowledge his or her own self-

worth.   It's not easy to admit we are worthy of our own pride
without feeling guilty for showing such obvious satisfaction with
ourselves.   Once again, hiding our personal satisfaction by eating
our reward is not an act of humility. You're not fooling anyone but
yourself.   It is not sinful or wrong to feel good about yourself and
your accomplishments.   Instead of choosing to eat your reward in
private, bask in the personal satisfaction you feel by "feeling" good
about who you are.   If you are unable to pat yourself on the back
without feeling guilt or wanting to celebrate with food, you have
won the battle.   However, if you are one of the many who cannot
enjoy "feeling" good about yourself independent of anyone else if
you feel the best way to reward yourself is through food, then
perhaps it's time to change your reward system and your way of
thinking.

The Flavor of Fluoride

You roll out of bed each morning and give very little thought to the ritual that follows - for most of us it involves brushing our teeth ...we enjoy that clean feeling - and appreciate the idea of keeping our teeth healthy. So, you might be surprised to learn just how many of us put off brushing our teeth after meals and even at night - Holding out.... Not willing to let go of the taste - not willing to acknowledge that our meal is truly over - not able to recognize our need to leave our eating options open - If I brush my teeth after each meal - I am drawing a line... I am finalizing the end of that food experience...for many of us, this feels like a punishment - The deprivation factor sets in.we want to wait as long as we can at night...what if I want a midnight snack...usually one falls asleep without brushing - after all, you might get hungry in the middle of the night. To some this sounds silly - To others, it's something they never really though about...or they simply chalked it up to laziness. Ask yourself this - Does the idea of brushing after each meal offend you - If I suggested that brushing after meals would significantly impact the way you think about food.... Would you take a toothbrush to work with you- the idea that we need the flavor of food to linger on our palates often sabotages our desire to learn healthier eating habits. We absolutely must stop using food as a reward and the end of meals as a punishment...brushing your teeth

after each meal gives you a physical conclusion to each meal -
However, it finalizes one eating experience...it does not
punish/deprive/or take away from your meal. Brushing after meals
is a healthy way to teach your body and your mind that food has a
time and a place in your life - however, food IS not AIR -we does
not need to eat 24/7 in order to exist.... Food does not dictate how
I feel, but my feelings have been dictated by the Food I eat for
many years - I must change the way I think about food or food will
change the way I respond to my surgery. Bariatric surgery is only
successful if we change our attitude and our eating habits. In my
practice, I see Bariatric clients who are struggling to maintain their
weight loss after surgery - Facing years of mental sabotage is
humbling when one has had the surgery and is not losing as they
hoped. Success is obtainable, but it is not inevitable. If you already
brush after meals -congratulations - That's one more habit that will
serve you well in maintaining a healthy weight loss - If not, please
consider my challenge: I challenge you to brush after each meal for
the next week. See how it feels - Is there resentment? Do you feel
angry or exposed? How do you feel about brushing after eating a
tasteful meal? If you feel nothing -if the experience is a pleasant
one - I encourage you to make it a lifetime habit. However, if you
find that the challenge creates anxiety, frustration, or perhaps denial
- I encourage you to be kind to yourself -recognize that you are
responding to feelings and not food.

By, Teri Kai Holtzclaw, Ph.D.   **39**

The more we acknowledge about what we think when it comes to eating, the easier it will be to change our thinking altogether.

Family Support

I got a phone call today. A concerned spouse wanted advice on how to support their loved one. This caller recognized that he/she was an intricate part of their partner's Bariatric success. We discussed all the ways family members could show their love and support - we also touched on some of the pitfalls that family and friends often stumble into...Here is a portion of the conversation's highlights. Try to respect the recovery process - when visiting in the hospital -Try to limit - if not eliminate- bringing fast food into the patient's room. Encourage your friend/family member to walk often. Decide to eat healthy and limit the amount of sweets/snacks/and high carbohydrate foods that come into the house. Do not undermine the patient's progress - encouraging the patient to just does this "try this" -or just "taste this"- or "you need to eat more." All these statements are detrimental to your friend/family member's success. If you are concerned or fearful that your loved one is not eating enough -and they are following their doctor's orders...Take a moment to acknowledge that your loved one has had major surgery to decrease their eating habits. It's okay to feel concern -even uncomfortably...after all, as your friend/family member changes his/her eating habits- they will also change how they view every aspect of their lives -This can be disconcerting to spouses, children and friends...when we change - we effect our current relationships.... We begin to really see how food monopolizes the most innocent of gatherings...church, Temple, school, reunions, business, pleasure...Food has been the center of our universe. There is nothing more liberating than the epiphany that FOOD is not really the center of the universe - it was only the center of our focus.... SIMPLY reset your sights...food falls into it's proper perspective...it is one of many details in life...it is not LIFE. The most important suggestion of supportive actions a friend/family member can do is to make the decision to Change with the patient...We can all find ways to improve our health -Anticipate that the eating rituals you all once shared will have to change ...perhaps you will need to be creative and decide to go the movies on Friday nights instead of your favorite buffet. Life is about making choices and relationships are what we choose to make them ...Embrace the changes -know that you're loved one is as curious, fearful and excited as you are to grow into the new and improved them.

A note to the Bariatric patient: We, as food people, don't include our family and friends in our decision to lose weight - we are often so caught up with our own shame.... Embarrassment and pain...we hid our excessive eating from everyone...eating alone.... We think we want to recover alone...food is not personal.... We are too involved to see it - but food is public domain...it's not a private indulgence -There is no secret -Food exposed you long before you made the choice to stop eating. Involve those who love you...allow your loved ones to participate in your success...hiding your weight loss...coveting the experience. You set your family up to unknowingly sabotage your goal. Food is not private...it is not the center of your universe.... And it will not replace the support you can have from those that love you enough to ask how they can help you succeed.

To Family and Friends

Although I have geared this book to the gastric bypass patient's point of view, I am aware of the numerous support persons out there that will purchase this text for guidance in assisting with their loved ones.   Open communication and honest interaction is essential to any relationship. It is of vital importance to remember that the patient is not on her or his journey alone. She or he changes their relational dynamic with everyone they encounter and know.   Nothing and no one is left unchanged in this physical metamorphosis. Thus, the mind body connection is taken a step further into global territory.

An important thing to remember when discussing your loved one's weight loss with them is that you are confronting their greatest secret. Be aware that she or he may feel a tremendous amount of fear related to their need to control their weight loss alone. You

should be prepared for that fear or more commonly, the anger they
will have in response to wanting to cover up their fear. Anything
you can say or do to alleviate that fear will help to enable that
person to hear your concerns.

TIME TO THINK

- Do you often feel guilty about your thoughts and actions
  surrounding food?
- When you are feeling guilty about your eating, do you let
  others know how you feel? If not, why?
- If you didn't feel guilty about overeating, are you still afraid
  you would do it again?
- Do you expect others to feel "bad" when they offer you
  more to eat without policing your intake for you?
- Do you make promises to yourself about your portions? If
  so, what were you afraid would happen if you no longer
  made promises?

<u>SOMETHING TO THINK ABOUT:</u>

- Guilt serves no purpose except to perpetuate a feeling of unhappiness.

- Our inability to trust ourselves is often manifested as guilt.

- We make promises to ourselves when we're not sure if we can truly commit to following through with our promise.

- Fear is the one component that keeps us from obtaining happiness at any cost.

- The results of our binge eating are the consequences of our actions. Not punishment for being bad people.

- We can begin our journey to healthy eating by finding healthy way to fulfill our starving need for happiness.

Ideas you may want to rethink:

- Guilt is what "stops the binging."

- Guilt is necessary to keep people honest about their eating disorder.

- If I don't feel guilty, I might binge-eat again.

- The only way to count on someone is to make her or him promise.

- When I let someone down, I'm responsible for her or his unhappiness.

Loving Yourself as much as You Love Others

Growing up my parents sacrificed a great deal for their children. They would often go without personal luxuries to satisfy our childhood wants and desires. I sometimes think about all the things my parents gave up in order to provide their children with the life they never had. Of course, any parent will tell you: "That's what parents do. You love your children. You place their needs above your own. That's parenthood." And my favorite: "You'll understand when you have kids of your own." This year, I finally felt I had reached that moment of Maternal Truth - Sandy and I are now proud parents of a beautiful puppy. And "yes." I do understand. There is nothing I wouldn't do for our precious baby girl. No sacrifice too large for this incredible puppy being placed in our care. Granted, a puppy is no comparison to rearing a child, but the point is to understand unconditional love not to debate the authentic definition of parenthood. Which brings me to the main topic of this article. Parenthood and your "first born." Everyday in my private practice I hear Mother's and Father's discuss the importance of caring for their children. I have yet to hear one individual stumble over the "value" of their little ones. It is an innate part of human nature to want to nurture and protect our offspring. It is one of our best qualities as human beings. Yet,

time and time again, I am met with incredulous indifference when I
ask the forbidden question. "Why not treat yourself as you would
your children? Why not place as much importance on what you do
and say as you would on your children's thoughts and actions? "
Consider this. If your child comes home angry or frustrated about
her homework - Do you immediately offer her food? Or are a hug
and some positive encouragement more appropriate to the
situation? If your child eats all her dinner and tells you she is full -
Do you fill her plate again anyway because you know it's her
favorite dish? Or do you trust that the favorite meal will be had
again at another time and let the leftovers go? If your child wants
to celebrate an outstanding report card - Do you feed her ice cream
until she finishes the box and can no longer move without hurting -
or do you take some extra time out to go play ball with her? As
you can see, we don't treat our bodies half as well as we treat the
bodies that we care for. Loving our own bodies does not
compromise the love we have for our children. Loving our bodies,
being willing to sacrifice our wants and desires for the good of our
health. Treating ourselves as if we are our "First born." This is just
good sense. We wouldn't force our children to eat themselves sick -
And we certainly wouldn't ask our children to replace the
unconditional love they have for us with food. We don't want our
children to struggle climbing up a flight of stairs or squeezing into
an airplane seat. We love them with all our hearts. Stop hiding
behind the rhetoric. I confront many of my clients on a daily basis

By, Teri Kai Holtzclaw, Ph.D. 47

regarding loving themselves. 90% of the time I am immediately told that I am wrong. The client is convinced that she loves herself. After all, we are conditioned to believe that we "see" inside - we know how "special" we are beneath the layers of fat surrounding us. Wrong. We can't see ourselves because we have lied to ourselves for so long that we can't even read the writing on the wall. Fact. We love our children. Fact. We would never do to our children what we choose to do to ourselves. Fact. We all need to ask ourselves do we love our own bodies as much as we love our first-born and if not. Why?

Self-Esteem

Self-Esteem is how we feel about ourselves; it is how we see ourselves when we look in the mirror. It affects every aspect of our lives - How we think, act and feel, and how we relate to others. Self-esteem comes from a lifetime of experiences and relationships. Family, home, school, work and social life all contribute to our self-worth. If you feel good about yourself in most areas of your life, you probably have good self-esteem. If you feel bad about yourself in most places, then your sense of self may be suffering. Even if you only feel bad in certain areas - you may like how well you do your job, but feel bad about your appearance - you can take simple steps to change your life for the better.

Creating Self-Esteem

Don't let past failures or negative thoughts hold you back. By learning to feel good about yourself, you can alleviate depression, stress and loneliness. Many of us have spent our lifetimes feeding our self-esteem with food and not even recognizing that we were trading out our self-worth for self-indulgence. Once we remove food from the equation, many of us are left with poor or no self-esteem. This lack of self-confidence and sense of individual value can leave us feeling empty and without purpose.

To begin creating self-esteem, one should look at her/his
strengths. Make a list of things you do well. List the reasons other
people like you. Ask a friend to help if you're having trouble
knowing what these things are. Ask yourself what you like about
yourself and write that down too. By actually writing these things
down, you can see your strengths. Focus on your good qualities
and use affirmations or positive statements everyday. Choose to
spend time with people who help you feel good about yourself.
Avoid people who are negative or put you down. Remember, the
healthier your relationships are, the faster your self-esteem will rise.

Successful Self-Esteem

Only you can set yourself up for success! Do things that help you
feel good about yourself. I believe each new positive experience
will help counteract an old negative experience. Try new things.
Make new friends. Go outside and play. Don't expect perfection.
Let you be a novice at something and enjoy the act of "learning"
something new and exciting.

Try This

Everyone has ups and downs, good days and bad days. But, given the choice, who wouldn't prefer to feel good? By using the following techniques you can learn how to enjoy life more, and turn those bad days into good ones in no time.

Body Work

A massage or relaxing day in the park can be physical pleasures that make life worth living. Enjoy regular physical activity such as taking walks, playing sports or simply enjoying the outdoors, to uplift your spirits.

Support Systems Work

A support network is a group of people you can turn to for comfort, a sympathetic ear, or good ideas. A support network can include family members, friends, coworkers, or anyone who cares about you. Reach out and make your network wider; you'll be glad you did.

Make Time

Making time for fun is like taking extra vacations throughout the
year. What are your favorite amusements? Movies, day trips into
the country, going to a fair can all be fun. Get out of your chair and
get going! You'll feel good before, during and after.

Helping Others

Few things give more pleasure than helping others. Find out about
some of the programs in your community that need your help. Try
something unlike any-thing you've ever done. It will enrich your life
with new ideas, information and feelings.

Practice

You can get in the habit of feeling good by being good to yourself
and others. When you care about yourself, you'll find that life holds
more meaning and pleasure.

Passion for Positives

Have you ever got out of bed in the morning and thought what a
lousy day it was going to be and found that it was just as bad as you
had imagined. Were you surprised that it did turn out bad, you
shouldn't have been, you had pre-programmed internally that it
would be bad, so it was.

Have you ever thought you would fail at something and you did.
Again it should not be a surprise because again you had pre-
programmed yourself.

Have you ever faced a difficult situation, but been determined to
succeed, worked out how to get what you wanted and got it. If you
have then ask yourself what was different in the last example from
the first two.

The answer of course is a positive outlook. So often we set
ourselves up to fail simply by the attitude that we take from the
outset. A positive attitude is important in maintaining success
weight loss after surgery. A "passion for positives" is a term I
coined when working with clients who are hesitant to change their
negative thinking. The point is to create a strong emotional
connection to changing your programming. We can all connect
passion with some highly charged experience in our lives. The
same intensity of passion is required to successfully recover from
past programming and reset our minds to think positively. Here's a
simple exercise to find out if you can improve on your "passion for

positives." Draw three columns on a sheet of paper. In the first
column, write several things you would like to happen. "I'd like to
eat smaller portions." "I'd like to control my access to trigger
foods." Then, close your eyes and listen to how you respond to
each item. Write your self-talk in the second column: (Example: "I
just can't do it." "It's too hard." " I've done this before.") In the
third column, write down a thought, which is the opposite of the
one in column two. Look over your list. If column two is more
positive than column three, you're already on your way to being
passionate about being positive. If column two is more negative,
look at column three for a more helpful, healthier response. Practice
choosing positive internal talk. You'll feel happier, more confident,
and less stressed.

Reflection

If you are able to look at "the big picture," you'll gain greater peace
of mind about maintaining your weight loss. Take time to think
about what has happened, why you had surgery in the first place,
and what it might mean. You might realize that your feelings are
mixed. For example, if you've been embarrassed about your size in
the past, you might be pleased with the weight loss, but
uncomfortable about the added attention from strangers and your
friends. You may feel sad or angry about having to let go of familiar
coping skills and poor eating habits. With time, those feelings will

change. Talking to trusted friends, family members, a therapist, or
health professional may speed the process.

Remember

No one can escape change. Accepting the fact that change has
taken place is important. When you take steps to think positively,
reflect on your decision and make your weight loss a permanent
condition, you will find acceptance easier. These steps will help you
successfully make the change part of your life.

Stay Calm

Calmness is the ideal state in which we should eat and participate in
any food related experience. Nervousness is the opposite of
calmness, and can often interfere with our desire to maintain healthy
eating behaviors. Strong emotions can evoke physical reactions
that may upset our balance and before we know it we are falling
into old eating habits. Binge-eaters often express a feeling of
"surprise" when she or he realizes they have indulged in a particular
trigger food without recognizing the warning signs. A good rule of
thumb is to create a calm environment when eating a meal. Take
your time. Eat slowly and allow your body to digest as you enjoy
your food experience. Setting a tone for mealtimes can often be
accomplished by playing soothing music or dimming the lights.

Mealtimes should be flexible and not stressful. A helpful tip to
remember is that when emotional moments occur, it's sometimes
best to wait before dining. Calm your nerves first. Sit for ten
minutes in peaceful reflection and allow your heart rate to return to
a normal state. Once calm, separate your eating experience from
your emotional experience.
It's important to realize that our body is highly sensitized to our
emotional well-being. Taking care of both is essential to taking
care of you.

Food and Loneliness

Like hunger, loneliness is a signal. Feeling lonely tells us that we
need emotional nourishment much the same way that feeling hungry
tells us that our body needs food. One must learn to discern the
difference between the signal for emotional nourishment and the
signal for physical nourishment. Everyone feels lonely some of the
time. Some people feel lonely all of the time. The majority of us
have used food to cope with our feelings of loneliness and numb
out the emotion. Many of us can no longer identify loneliness
because we have conditioned our bodies to anticipate the feeling -
and stuff it down with large quantities of food. Medical studies
have shown that isolation can lead to problems such as depression,
physical illness and alcoholism. Taking steps to overcome
loneliness will make you happier and healthier. No one needs to

live with ongoing loneliness. The best way to combat loneliness is to "change" your lifestyle. Take care of yourself. Try to look your best. You will feel better about yourself, and it will be easier to get to know people. Try something you've always wanted to do, but keep putting off. Make plans to take a class or join a club. Avoid escapes. Television and novels are great sources of entertainment, but be careful not to use them to avoid social contact. If you are using alcohol or drugs to help you feel less lonely seek professional help immediately. If you are unable to make a lifestyle change or feel overwhelmed by your feelings of loneliness, seek help from a therapist, doctor, or other professional.

Ten Ways To Take Better Care of Yourself

The ten principles below can form the basis of a plan to help you take better care of yourself and help you maintain successful weight loss after surgery.

1. Adopt a healthier frame of mind. If you haven't already done so, reassess your assumptions about how the world works. We are each unique individuals with imperfect traits. You must recognize that what you know is what got you to where you are today. It's time to let go of what you "know" and recreate your perception of yourself and how you relate to others.

2. Develop a plan. Keep a record of your healthy eating habits and keep track of your progress. Know what a normal portion size is and when you are increasing or decreasing your portions. Keep a food journal and weigh yourself on a regular basis. Know your body and your triggers. A plan helps us to regain control quickly and easily when we regress to our old eating behaviors. And we are human. We are not perfect. We ALL need a plan.

3. Have a plan for a variety of different crises. Each of us have creative ways of sabotaging our weight loss success. Make sure you have a plan for all of your self-inflicted pitfalls.

4. Control your access to food - and take it seriously. Controlling your access to binge-foods is important, for both physical and psychological reasons. After all, not all of us can identify our behaviors before the damage has been done. So while you should trust your ability to "not overeat," there's no reason not to reinforce your will power with common sense.

5. Consider including your support system in your success. The idea of including others in your recovery from an eating disorder may sound frightening. However, I assure you that it is a very empowering experience to ask for and allow someone to be a part of your weight loss journey. Loved ones want to help you. It is certainly not their responsibility to "police" your eating habits, but it

is their responsibility to support you in your decision to eat in a
healthy way.

6.   Consider trying something new.   It's time to expand your
portfolio of experiences.   Try something new to reinforce your
decision to maintain your weight loss and not slip back into old
eating habits.   Go to the gym or attend a yoga class.   Learn
healthier ways to cook or join a walking group at work.   Be
creative.

7. Reevaluate your current environment. This is especially true for
those of us who have lived our lives surrounded by unhealthy
people and behaviors. Change your world. The first step is to have
a plan to make small changes. Clean out the refrigerator and refill it
with healthy foods that support your new eating habits.   Cook
healthier meals and eat out less.   The small changes create huge
results.

8. Reevaluate your daily activities. Do you eat on a regular basis
and maintain a healthy lifestyle or do you skip meals and snack on
the wrong items? Do you take vitamins daily or do you often
forget or decide it's not necessary? Think about the choices you
make each day and how you can improve your eating habits.

9. Don't forget about denial. Recognize that the biggest threat to

your weight loss success is denial. Denial can cause far greater damage than any other issue. We are experts at avoiding confrontation with our problems and with people, and instead, turning to food. Denial is one of our finest defense mechanisms and we can even fool ourselves. Don't get caught in your own web of deceit. Know yourself.

10. Manage your food -don't be managed by it. Above all, don't be overcome by fear. Paralysis would be the worst reaction to managing your food. For one thing, it could cause you to give up on your goal of weight loss success - just what you don't need after having weight loss surgery. You have got to take responsibility for managing your food. Be accountable for your right choices and embrace the opportunity to succeed where you have never succeeded before.

If you don't have weight maintenance or weight loss goals, you'll lose or maintain nothing. If maintaining or losing weight after weight loss surgery doesn't appeal to you, you have a problem. Namely, you wanted nothing from weight loss surgery but a short-term fix to a long-term eating disorder. This more than likely means that you are unhappy with yourself. And if you're not, you probably should be. I highly recommend having weight loss and weight maintenance goals, then breaking them down into manageable bits that you can achieve each week. This may sound

like a lot of work, but the discipline carries over into the other parts
of your life. Right now I am working on increasing my ability to
meditate. My goal is to be able to relax and release stress for
longer periods of time. Progress may take a few months, but I've
made the time.

The Evil "E" Word

Exercise improves self-esteem. If you suffer from low or poor self-worth, exercise may be the answer. Many of us have spent years training our bodies and our minds to "resist" the evil "E" word. I have spent decades running from exercise. I had convinced myself over the years that exercise is fine for those who enjoy it, but it's just not for those of us who don't want to start. It involves self-discipline, responsibility and commitment. Amazingly enough, many obesity patients, including myself, struggle with these traits when applying them to our own lives. Once again, we meet at the crossroads of change: In order to create change in our lives, we must choose to do that which we have chosen NOT to do for so long. Doing things we don't like to do is a part of growing up and becoming responsible healthy adults. It's time to CHOOSE to exercise. Exercise will benefit your physical health and your mental health. It is a key factor in increasing self-esteem and confidence.

Artificial Life Sweeteners

Many of us choose to artificially sweeten our lives with lies about "why" we eat, "what" we eat and "how much" we eat. We replace REAL feelings with Artificial ones and we're perplexed as to why we can't stop eating. We refuse to acknowledge our own responsibility for sweetening our lives by artificial means. We can't figure out, after all that fake sweetener substitute, why we feel so emotionally hungry. I believe, not unlike the research surrounding the physical reaction our bodies may have to artificial sweeteners - That our mental reaction can be just as dramatic. Cease the "artificial" living. Stop replacing your integrity, your fears, your emotions and your pain with artificial sweeteners.

Misery is Inevitable?

Recently, I spoke with an individual who sees gastric bypass surgery in an entirely different light then I do. She declared without apology that she hated people like me. "You take something that's terrible," she said flatly, "and make believe it's beautiful." She continued. "Obesity is a horrible disease in this country. People are cruel and insensitive. The world needs to change, not us!" She remarked incredulously.

I considered her point of view for a moment. "Did you ever consider," I asked softly, "that you might be taking something beautiful and making believe it's terrible?"

At that moment, I realized that neither one of us held the answer, only a perception that we each had created and then used to embrace our situation. I had decided to see my eating disorder as an opportunity to grow, learn and love. She regarded her obesity as a curse. Our different experiences had followed from those distinctly different points of view.

Wanting to reach out to her, I told her that I, too, was once overwhelmed and devastated by my weight. I remember the taunting and endless fat jokes in my teenage years. I remember crying alone in my bedroom for hours. And I remember overcompensating for my size by becoming popular and serving as president of the Drama club. I remember the mixed messages of being told I was "beautiful" and knowing I had dates, but still knowing that I was fat. "They" told me my weight didn't matter...but it did! And on some level, that denial, that lie, permeated in every part of who I strived to become.

I believe the way we see the world does create the world we see. I tried to explain how the world had changed for me, in significant and irrevocable ways, once I had changed my own view of my life and begun to make happiness and love priorities. As a result, I was able to greet my choice to have gastric bypass surgery as a wonderful opportunity.

The woman with the different point of view listened to my sharing without comment. Finally, she laughed at my unending enthusiasm. She decided I had been well intentioned but, nonetheless, naïve and unrealistic in my hopefulness and happiness. She questioned the validity of my attitude. Ultimately, she preferred what she called her reality. I feel more comfortable and peaceful in my body today than I have ever before. I created a powerful attitudinal advantage for myself. Each of us can, in a simple way and an easy way, access an amazing attitudinal advantage within ourselves once we come to understand that happiness and love is a choice and misery is optional -not inevitable. Because we have trained our minds to protect our obesity for so long, we cannot expect our mental habits to be broken once the fat is removed. The attitude transformation involves a great deal of effort and energy on your part. Unlike the surgery that relies on the skill of a surgeon, the attitude adjustment

relies on the skill of the patient. Choose happiness. Celebrate your
success. You don't need a reason to be happy. Happiness is a state
of mind - Not a reward. It's a God given right offered to every one
of us for simply existing.

Priorities and Happiness

The events of September eleventh two thousand and one have
inspired many of us to "redefine" our priorities. Some of us have
used this new priority system to invalidate or negate our decision to
have weight loss surgery. Somehow, we have placed our own
health and ourselves at the bottom of our list. We have made the
choice to make ourselves unworthy of good health and abundant
happiness in an effort to validate or lift up someone else's agenda.
It breaks my heart to see so many good reasons to claim misery and
unhappiness. Reasons and excuses are interchangeable. There is
no noble or valiant reason why one would not choose happiness
over misery.

If just one person changes, becomes happier, touches another with
a more loving and peaceful heart, then the world has, indeed,
become a more pleasant place. If each of us acknowledges our
personal responsibility to a greater network of interaction, then, like
the stone dropped in a pond, our changes will cause countless
ripples. Our capacity to change enables us to make a truly
profound difference in the world. When one person overcomes a

fear or obstacle in their lives, all those around that person are touched and inspired by her or his triumphs. For many of us, gastric bypass surgery is a part of our journey towards happiness. As we become happier, our relationships change, and our happiness impacts the lives of many. If happiness means that we become easier, more comfortable with ourselves, more accepting, respectful, excited and appreciative of what we do and with whom we spend time with, would we not then become a gift to all those we meet? Would we not become a wonderful gift to ourselves as well? I strongly encourage each of us to go back and align our new list of priorities with the greater picture. Validate your self worth and realize that you are a powerful force within your community. If each of us made our first priority to bring the gift of personal happiness to the lives of those we embrace - The effect would be phenomenal.

Seasonal Stress

As the holiday seasons approach, our minds and hearts turn to gift giving, great social get-togethers and lots of family time. With all that we wish to accomplish during this season, time can become a precious commodity. Much physical, emotional and financial energy is expended in our sincere efforts to make all our family and friends feel loved. Unfortunately, this can sometimes come at the expense of our own health and enjoyment of the season. What I propose we do each season is make a few small changes to the way we go about experiencing the Holidays every year.

Before you begin to immerse yourself in the Holiday festivities, it's important to have a clear idea of your goals and priorities. Is one of your goals to maintain a positive holiday spirit and to spread good cheer? Or is one of your priorities simply to eat right and exercise, thereby minimizing the stress involved in seasonal tasks? Think about what you would like to accomplish as a parent, a spouse, a sibling or a friend. Once you understand your personal goals and priorities for the holidays it becomes easier to select activities that support those goals. During the Holidays, we all have more things to do with less time to do it! One thing all successful time management gurus agree on is the fact that goals are essential to good time management. True goals involve an investment of time, energy, possible sacrifice, and true commitment.

A wish list consists of waiting for a miracle. Separate your goals from your wish list. Focus on balance. It's important that you choose and prioritize Holiday goals that will minimize your stress and maximize your enthusiasm for accomplishing the activity. Last but not least, learn to say no. Saying yes to everything that is asked of you is ridiculous and yet many people do it everyday. You cannot possibly do everything for everyone. You have to make choices. Listen to the request and be sure you understand it. If you feel the request is outside of your goals and priorities, abilities or time frames, say no clearly and explain why. Don't feel guilty because you can't do everything.

TIME TO THINK

Take A Moment and answer these questions.

- Are you happy? Do you binge-eat when you are happy?

- Is unhappiness necessary now in order to gain happiness later?

- Does fear of overeating factor in to your ability to be happy?

- Will "thinking" about happiness make it happen for you? What about "thinking" about eating differently from the way you eat today?

- Is what you desire what you need? What foods do you desire the most? Do you need them?

- Is happiness a priority in your life? DO you connect food with happiness?

- When is it okay for you to experience personal happiness without connecting it to food?

- What does my happiness have to do with my weight loss?

Here is a list of key points to think about as you meditate upon your answers:

- We are all doing the best we can with the best of what we have in the moment.

- Unhappiness is sometimes necessary to break old patterns and introduce us to new ones.

- You are your own best friend. An expert on what you think and feel. Trust your inner voice.

- You do know what's good for you.

- We all deserve happiness.

- We think clearly when we are truly happy. And our eating habits improve.

- Happy individuals have direction in their lives.

- You are what you think.

- You can be everything you ever wanted to be by believing in who you are today.

Ideas you may want to rethink:

- Unhappiness makes me appear intelligent and more serious about my life.

- If my happiness isn't sacrificed, then what's the point?

- If I'm not striving towards happiness - what will I have to look forward to?

- Only stupid people are happy all the time.

- The unhappier I am -the better person God believes me to be.

- If I don't wallow in enough misery, I won't ever change my circumstances.

- You can't teach an old dog new tricks.

- Change is too hard.

- Happiness makes me eat more.

- Unhappiness takes away my appetite.

- Eating avoids confrontation.

THE MAGIC PILL A Mental Health Companion for the Gastric Bypass Patient

By, Teri Kai Holtzclaw, Ph.D.

PART III

LONGEVITY

Decision Made

You did it! You made the decision to have weight loss surgery - a physical transformation that will soon change your life, as you know it. You are already fantasizing about the new wardrobe, new job and new relationships that await you. It's as if you've been given a second chance at living. Good for you!

Weight Loss Surgery is gaining momentum throughout the world as a new and innovative tool to lose weight. It works! Five years ago, weighing in at approximately 300 pounds, I made the decision to have gastric bypass surgery. It changed my life! Weight loss brings so much more than just a smaller body frame. Because our culture is obsessed with our body image, we find ourselves losing more than just weight. The stigma of being an overweight person stifles advancement in our careers, relationships, families and communities. Previously closed doors mysteriously open for the newly thin individual. It is an eye opening and thoroughly sense provoking experience. Every part of you is ignited with the possibilities that line up for the "new and improved" you.

The physical transformation is quick and dramatic. The weight falls off and you begin to experience immediate feedback from yourself and others. However, as the title of my first book so

By, Teri Kai Holtzclaw, Ph.D.   **76**

delicately put it, THIS is NOT Brain Surgery! Your mind stays in tact as is. For the majority of us who have lived two thirds of our lives as obese, oppressed and ostracized individuals, this can be the heartbreaker. We are keenly aware of how our mental faculties affect our physical bodies. We know that when we celebrate -we eat, when we mourn -we eat, when we laugh, cry, play, hurt and disappoint -we eat.

We numb our senses to the point that we can eat past our "fullness" stage right into feeling sick and nauseated. Often, this feeling is represented by a condition called "reflux," a physical condition that we acknowledge, but we don't connect to our emotional illness. It is an emotional illness to replace everything we feel with food. It is an emotional illness to decide to lose weight physically and not to recognize that our emotional health will continue to sabotage our physical health -no matter what temporary physical alteration we make.

Food inhalation is an illness that cannot be cured by Weight Loss Surgery alone. You must combine ALL your resources and address ALL the parts of YOU that have been affected by your weight gain. This includes your physical body and your mental body -The mind. Your brain is like a computer that works off of programs you created over years of experiences as overweight individual. The program pulls from your insight as a large person and makes choices for you based on previous reasoning. The choices we make as obese human beings do not serve us well as thin human beings. In fact, they are obsolete. However, our minds, like computers, do not tell you to re-program them. You have to create an entire new program for your mind to run on.

It's true that it's easier to learn something new than to unlearn something old. You have to make the decision to radically change your mind's body with your physical body. This is not a popular phrase amongst my clients. Changing our minds, creating new programs, letting go of old thinking - all these things require effort, commitment and personal responsibility for our own actions. The surgery itself is embedded in the Physical body -the same way we numb our emotions and disconnect with food; we can numb our emotions and feel "disconnected" from the physical procedure of surgery. If we can manage to lose our weight WITHOUT emotional investment, weight that we gained THROUGH emotional investment, then we have successfully AVOIDED the very parts of us we had intended to avoid in the first place.

I believe the concept I just described is what overweight Americans find so appealing about weight loss surgery. We are sold on the idea that we can lose the weight without acknowledging responsibility for our weight gain. It's been my experience with clients that many overweight individuals' battle "responsibility" issues in multiple facets of their lives. We create programs for our minds to pull from. These programs are used in our financial decisions, career moves and relationships. Ultimately, if we program our brains to avoid responsibility for our eating, our brains learn to avoid responsibility for other things, as well. You cannot divide your brain. You must choose integrity in all areas of your life. I often speak on the issue of integrity because I've learned that dishonesty begins with food and then spreads throughout your character.

I cannot choose when to be honest with my eating, you and myself without flubbing up in one area or another at one time or another. Ultimately, I create a program of dishonesty that becomes easier and easier to pull from in times of stress. It's a sobering feeling to realize that weight loss surgery is only one part of obtaining and maintaining successful weight loss. It's easy to fall into our old programming of feeling defeated and overwhelmed at the prospect of having to do something outside of our comfort zone. All too often, I have clients come in to my office pleading with me to give them that secret anecdote that "excuses" them from taking responsibility for their mental health.

You, and you alone, have the power to change your mind. The way you think about food is not going to change unless you change the way you think. Contrary to our fantasies, we are not powerless over our physical transformation, either. No matter how we convince ourselves that we are not connected to the actual surgical procedure, such as gastric bypass surgery, we are. We are active participants in all parts of our lives.

We can and have programmed ourselves to deny these facts -reassuring ourselves that because the skilled surgeons are doing the intricate procedure ON our bodies - we are no longer responsible FOR our bodies. We have no fear when it comes to surrendering our physical fat - and we have no courage when it comes to releasing our mental girth. You have a brain full of useless information after weight loss surgery. You have spent years reacting to every feeling and emotion with food. You are heart broken when you learn that your old way of handling stress, excitement, pain, joy, fear and depression is no longer an option. You cannot choose food to fill every void in your life any longer. And you can't choose to avoid those voids without realizing just how heart broken you are to lose food as a viable option.

Revealing your addiction to food is a painful experience before and after weight loss surgery. The difference is that after weight loss surgery, when we begin to lose the physical weight, the mental weight becomes heavier and the addiction becomes clearer.

Many of us believe that if we lose the physical weight we will miraculously shed ourselves of food addiction. This is not true. A food addict, not unlike an alcoholic who no longer drinks alcohol, is always a food addict. Losing weight will not make one lose the desire to eat through the same emotional experiences that lead you to overeating in the first place. Once again, weight loss surgery is a physical transformation and not a mental one. The mind stays in tact while the body is propelled forward into an incredibly exciting new and thinner you.

THE MAGIC PILL A Mental Health Companion for the Gastric Bypass
Patient

The beginning of your weight loss surgical experience is full of euphoric feelings of relief and hopefulness. You immediately begin to shed pounds and reveal a thinner and culturally popular look. Your outward appearance inspires a new urgency within to build your wardrobe, care for your hair and make up - even develop an entirely new look. Your time is consumed with a new addiction, a temporary obsession with creating a physically pleasing manifestation of who you are. This is an exciting time!

Once you begin to acclimate to your new body, and as your physical scars begin to heal, your mind is given the opportunity to test-drive the new and thinner you. The morsel of food that once filled your newly made pouch (stomach) no longer "feels" like enough. "Feel" and "Fill" are interchangeable words in the food addict's mental programming.

I believe in order to grasp the difference between our "feelings" and what "fills" our pouches (stomachs) we have to be able to identify those times when we are emotionally hungry instead of physically hungry. It's not enough to acknowledge a connection between our mental body and our physical body. We must be able to discern where one begins and the other ends. Physical hunger "feels" different than emotional starvation. Can you tell the difference?

I often teach my clients to meditate before eating. This accomplishes two very important things. First, it slows down the mind and body and allows one to focus on the task at hand. A meal requires a food addicts "full" attention -so that we know when we are "full." Second, it gives one time to decide if she needs to "fill" her stomach or "feel" her emotions. It is imperative that we learn to experience emotions without food to enhance or cover up these unfamiliar feelings. Life is not to be avoided. Feelings are to be embraced and passionately sought out. Many of us spend a lifetime wanting to know unconditional love; however, we fear all the emotions that help us reach that state of maturity to obtain such a lofty and satisfying goal.

In my private practice, I offer several workbooks to clients who want to change their thinking patterns and reprogram the way they manage their weight loss. In these workbooks, I offer exercises on how to identify and define your own mental saboteurs. Mind games are what we play on ourselves when we decide we are going to eat before we decide if we need or want to eat.

One mind game that seems to be played by most of us is the idea that "food is necessary" as long as it revolves around family and friends. The cultural norm feeds this notion and continues to nurture it with television and similar types of propaganda. I am not insinuating that food has not had a valuable impact on Religion, Politics or Family gatherings. I am insisting that food is NOT necessary just because we are in the company of family and friends. Celebrations, Funerals, Graduations, Holidays -the list is endless. I can legitimately come up with a "special" reason why I should be able to deviate from my eating plan every day of the week for an entire year. Birthdays, Anniversaries, Social activities and on and on it goes.

I am usually confronted, and bitterly, when I bring up the idea of NOT eating at every gathering/function with incredulous reasons why I am out of my mind for even suggesting such blasphemy.

The top three reasons I am out of my mind are:

- "It's rude not to eat when everyone else is eating."

- "It's rude not to bring something to eat, and I make such great pastries!"

- "You can't ask me not to eat something! What would people think?"

These three reasons illustrate one simple point. Each reason is based solely on what others might think and not one reason addressed a need for food because of physical hunger. Every reason illustrated a need for emotional acceptance by family and friends and outright fear of being without food during such an important event. We use food to manage experiences in our lives instead of using communication to let others know why we are choosing not to eat.

Repeat this phrase out loud everyday: " I am not hungry." It sounds like a silly request. I am baffled why we are so afraid to say this phrase in public settings. I understand that when we were struggling with obesity and feeling ashamed, we did not want to call attention to ourselves - especially not to our eating selves. But, after weight loss surgery, why the dilemma? Why are we afraid to be honest about our lack of hunger?

When I was a young child, my family often "rewarded" itself with food. Some of my fondest family memories are wrapped around wonderful feasts and delightful desserts. I always understood the "ritual" of eating to be sacred and good. Years of reinforcement have embedded this food reward system in to every part of my Being. I learned that the food reward system is used in Corporate America - retirement lunches, promotion parties, office potlucks, annual conferences, as well as Little League America where children are rewarded for sportsmanship and a good game with ice cream and sodas.

Once again, we have weight loss surgery to lose weight physically. The surgery is to help us eat less and, therefore, weigh less. However, if we choose to "out eat" our surgery (and it is being done) we will ultimately gain the weight back. It is a painfully heart wrenching experience to watch someone lose all their weight and choose to gain it back. Your mind must change with your physical appearance. The idea of eating as a reward, and not because of physical hunger, is deceiving. You are lying to yourself and your body. Each morsel of food you place in your mouth, without feeling hungry first, lies to your physical body and programs your mental body to eat regardless of how you feel. Mixing "filling" with "feeling" is an avoidance mechanism that is no longer useful to you. Stop doing it! Feel your emotions. Feed your physical hunger. Do not do both - and do not do either if you can't discern which one is happening at the moment.

Put me in a room with a group of successful weight loss clients who are talking about food and I know I will be intrigued. No matter what their "mind magic" is, there is one thing I can count on when I listen to successful weight loss clients' talk - I will hear confidence, energy and passion for life! Loving your life is the best way to become successful at almost any goal. Knowing how to convey your love of life through communication is the best way to become successful in weight loss maintenance.

Explaining weight loss surgery can seem difficult, because so much of what we experience is complicated, nonverbal or just painful. Often, we are not comfortable with explaining what we did to obtain weight loss; however, we say we are willing to do anything to maintain our weight loss. This - is Anything.

Lie about your surgery, be dishonest about your surgery, hide your surgery; all of these things are detrimental to your weight loss maintenance. Your character suffers from each deception.

Every lie eats away at your integrity and ultimately your Being. The body is an outward manifestation of the mind. Lies and deceit will reveal themselves in places that feed our shame and embarrassment - most of us call that place: "Our waist." Honesty within is worn without.

Instead of feeling tongue-tied, imagine if the next time someone asked you what you did to lose weight, you could make eye contact, smile and, using one or two sentences, convey just the right words to answer with integrity and candor:

"I had weight loss surgery. It was the best decision I ever made to change my body and my mind. I am happy and healthy for the first time in decades."

Calming your internal anxiety is one important step in becoming optimistic and motivated about managing your long-term weight loss success. It also helps to have the support of others. You need to surround yourself with people who will encourage your physical health and mental well-being. You need to have support that energizes you instead of discourages you.

Many of us visualize the "perfect body" for ourselves and leave out the visualization of what our minds will do to enhance and support this perfect physique. We only focus on what we can see and not on what we can feel. Ironically, what we feel impacts a large percentage of how we perceive something through sight.

The myth that we, as weight loss surgery patients, are obsessed with our physical appearance is ludicrous. We, a group who has spent the majority of our time hiding from public attention, do not suffer from an obsession with our physical bodies - quite the contrary. It is our determination to avoid and ignore our bodies that has gotten us to this point. And it is the realization of our newfound "perfect body" that has inspired us to take interest, some for the first time, in our physical appearance overall.

Granted, the body perfect is in the eye of the beholder. And looking into her own mirror, she sees a body perfect. You and you alone must come to peace with the body that you have. This peace is developed in your mind and nurtured in your soul. Be kind to yourself. Change your mind to fit inside your body, comfortably. Reprogram your thoughts to be encouraging and not disparaging.

A positive attitude will impact your physical health. Do not fool yourself into thinking that there is no connection between beating yourself up and out-eating your surgery. Negative attitudes will build into a depression and your mind will program itself to repeat negative behaviors through every aspect of your life. It is a destructive and unnecessary cycle.

The gym is one place we go to practice bodybuilding and develop our muscle tone. Bodybuilding also brings up visions of aerobics, swimming and various other exercises. The body building techniques described in this chapter are focused on one muscle - your Brain. By now, you may have realized that I am convinced our minds and bodies are connected and impact one another in virtually every way possible. A healthy mind affects a healthy body and a healthy body cannot be sustained without a healthy mind to maintain it. Mind body building techniques are useful in several ways. First, they will reduce stress and increase your capacity for energy. Second, if practiced on a daily basis, these simple exercises will tone and strengthen your ability to think, feel and identify emotional reactions before they occur. Identifying our emotional reactions is important because we tend to REACT with food.

The first exercise is one we are all-familiar with, but have never taken seriously enough to act on - until now. Now is the time to act without giving in to our emotions. Program your mind to do this exercise regardless of your emotional reaction to it.

I want you to choose one of the three affirmations I have listed below and decide to say it out loud to yourself once a day for the next seven consecutive days.

1. I am beautiful.
2. I am loved and accepted just as I am.
3. I am happy.

Program your mind that this is not an optional exercise. You do not have to believe in the affirmation and you certainly do not have to consider it to be the Truth. Remember, affirmations create truth. Truth does not create affirmation.

The next exercise requires a great deal of courage and
acceptance on your part. It is time to define a new relationship
between yourself and food. No one sets out to be obese. Over
eating is about lack of control. Weight loss maintenance is about
reclaiming some of your control and returning the power to whom
it belongs. You gave ALL of your power over to food once. Now,
it's time to take that power back and decide that food belongs in a
less powerful position in your life.

For some of us, abandoning food is the ultimate betrayal. It
is similar to overturning our ruler. It is an act of rebellion against
the very thing that helped us avoid so many other parts of our lives.
It is not unusual to feel guilty about turning on food and rejecting
its power. Guilt is a reflection of our fear. We fear letting go of
food - It's like letting go of our lifeline to sanity. It is this dramatic.
It is this powerful. It is this controlling.

Defining a new relationship with food is simply drawing a
line in the sand and declaring war upon your own thought process.
Deny yourself the emotional satisfaction of disregarding everything
you've read in this book.
Deny yourself the emotional satisfaction of rationalizing why this
book does not apply in your circumstances. Deny yourself the
emotional satisfaction of acting on old programming when it no
longer applies to the new and improved you.

When I was a small child growing up in Bangkok, Thailand,
I had the rare opportunity of spending time with Buddhist monks.

Early in the morning, I would walk down the street to the local
vendor and I would get two balls of sweet sticky rice. I would then
share my rice with the Buddhist monks that would come each
morning to be fed. This ritual became a sacred and special time for
me. It brought me great joy to share what I had and to have such a
small gift so graciously accepted -as if I had offered a wonderful
feast. I tell you this story to illustrate two points.

The first point is that food is an international symbol of
peace and is to be honored for its power to bring nations and
people together. Food represents religious and community
connection and should be respected for its place in our society.

My second point is that food brings joy and happiness to
those who do not have it. Food is necessary to sustain life. It is a
part of our lives for as long as we each exist. Food is not
something we can avoid or walk away from. Food must be
honored, respected and managed.

There is a strong connection between food and our bodies.
The only weapon you have to manage this connection is your mind.
Use it. Make your mind work for you instead of against you. If
you are using your mind to beat yourself up for not having control
over your eating, can you imagine the power your mind could have
over controlling your eating? Are you willing to consider that
maybe there is another way to look at yourself and your weight
loss?

This new way of looking at yourself would involve

combining your knowledge of what you think and feel with your
knowledge of what you learned from this book and know to be
true. Teach yourself to ignore the emotional desire to eat when
you're feeling so many other things and you know hunger is not the
label on those feelings. You must make a conscious decision to
"change" your mind. Equip your physical body with a mind
programmed for long-term weight loss success.

I continue to be amazed by the people I meet who have had
weight loss surgery and assure me that my services are meaningless
and a waste of time in their situation. I do not solicit these remarks.
They come to me freely and without reservation by the parties
delivering the message. It is my hope that these individuals
understand the body connection and the awesome power our minds
have over our bodies.

Isn't it amazing in this day and age, when we are given only
one chance to live this life, that we are also given the medical
technology to make this one life healthier and happier?

Gratitude doesn't begin to express the overwhelming joy I
have experienced since my decision to have weight loss surgery
over five years ago. I now live in a body that allows me to follow
through with my dreams. Since weight loss surgery, I have traveled
the globe comfortably in a plane to Tokyo and on a train to
Moscow. I have enjoyed cruising the Caribbean and parasailing in
the Keys. I have learned how to ride a motorcycle and ski down
any bunny slope. Every day I am conquering a new and exciting

challenge that is possible because of my healthier state. I learned a
long time ago, as a young obese teenager that time does not repeat
itself. Once lived, it is gone. There is nothing sadder than looking
at an overweight, hurt, scared, disappointed and depressed
adolescent and realizing it's a reflection of who you were. We
wear obesity, not only on the outside, but also on the inside. I
believe obesity is a state of mind and a physical state of our bodies.
Lose the "filling" (the fat) and you're left with a lot of suppressed
"feelings." Keep the "feelings" and you're going to leave your
weight loss behind.

The body and the mind are connected to serve a purpose.
We are able to affect our healing and the general health of our
physical bodies by being mentally attuned. Doesn't it make sense
that losing our fat would need to be connected, as well? It's
important to shed the body weight along with the weight that we
carry on our shoulders. Once again, we, as food addicts, cannot
often discern between "filling" and "feelings." It's an enlightening
experience to learn that what we thought we would lose with our
weight remains in tact even when we become thin.

Becoming thin, after years of obesity, will not automatically
bring you love, passion, confidence, self-esteem or any of the other
emotionally healthy states that we all strive to achieve and maintain.
The illusion that a thin body will bring you peace of mind is just that
- an illusion. Wake up! A thin body, much like the surgery itself,
will open up new opportunities and give you more choices to

consider; however, none of these things act alone. You must step up to the plate and reclaim responsibility for your life.

Obesity and being overweight is about choosing to relinquish our power and giving up control to one thing -Food. Obtaining and maintaining weight loss after surgery is about making the choice to reclaim your power and return food to the submissive state in which it belongs.

Life is about choices and not necessarily about emotional gratification. We, as overweight individuals, do not like to hear that. Food stimulates that part of our minds that desires immediate gratification -not unlike the two-year-old child who has a temper tantrum when she can't have candy for dinner. We want what we want when we want it! Some of us abuse the freedom of being adults by choosing candy for dinner and answer to no one, as if to justify our childlike craving by hiding our adult actions.

Facing our fears is one of the hardest journeys upon which we will ever embark. Acknowledging that food has controlled our lives and that it's time to take responsibility for changing our minds is difficult. Prior to weight loss surgery, it was not unusual for me to hide in a restroom at work and sneak a candy bar. I was overweight and I didn't want other people to see me eating something unhealthy. I would join my co-workers for lunch, eat a sensible meal, and then take advantage of my next break to eat more. Of course, I would go out to the parking lot and sit in my parked car where no one could see me. This adult was acting like a

child who was afraid of being caught overeating. The irony is that
my body had given away my secret long before I had. It never
occurred to me that people would know I must have been eating
unhealthily - and a lot - in order to be gaining so much weight. I
was fooling no one. I was just acting like one.

Emotional wellness involves developing the skills to live life
well. Life throws challenges at all of us, but those that have better
coping skills tend to fare better in life.   Emotional wellness
encompasses many factors, including relating to others in positive
ways; learning and appreciating who you are as a person, including
your values and your strengths and vulnerabilities; learning to be an
effective problem-solver and critical thinker; and thinking
preventatively at all times by looking ahead a few steps and not just
reacting in the moment. So much hurt and pain could be prevented
if we thought ahead more and anticipated the consequences more
realistically.

We all have said it. We all believed it at one time or
another.   Some of us are still paying homage to its message,
without truly understanding the ramifications of what we are
saying. The words go something like this: " Why are people so
shallow? After all, I'm still the same person fat that I am thin."

I welcome the opportunity to respond to this inquiry. You
are not the same person! I repeat. You are not the same person!
You have changed your eating habits, which has affected your
schedule, your finances, your wardrobe and your interest in your

personal appearance. And the dominoes continue to fall. You
smile more, you exude greater confidence, you don't mind being
noticed as much, you react a little more boldly than before, and you
are able to do many things you never considered when you were
large. You are not the same individual! Overweight, you felt
awkward and embarrassed, got angry when victimized on an
airplane or at a restaurant. Overweight, you couldn't ride in a roller
coaster or run a marathon.

The thin you is an evolution of the fat you. Not a
reproduction. Do not be misguided by well meaning phrases from
your old way of thinking. Its only purpose is setting you up to have
a negative attitude about those around you. The thin you is a new
and exciting person. Let others in. Allow love to move freely
through your life. Don't limit your possibilities with judgment calls
and emotional game playing from your past. This is your time to
shine. Don't waste it.

People are not shallow. You are naïve. You are reciting a
phrase that was programmed into your thinking a long time ago by
some well-meaning individual.
You have not considered the definition behind the statement. You
are reacting to an emotion that is invoked each time someone treats
you differently.

Anger is the number one issue that comes up in my sessions
with clients exploring the long-term weight loss phenomena. We
experience anger at others for discriminating against us because we

are fat. We get mad when someone treats us badly and we want to victimize ourselves because of our size. Usually, our anger is justified. Again. Usually, our anger is justified.

This is where I interject the thing that you simply do not want to know. I have yet to come across one client who has not felt "exposed" by my direct confrontation of such an untouchable subject. There are some things one just doesn't come out and say.

Your anger will reveal itself on your body. Anger is a powerful emotion that cannot be hidden for long periods of time. Sooner or later, your anger will eat at you until you have gained back every pound you thought you physically lost. Let it go. Find purpose and find peace, but do not replace food with anger. It will destroy you.

Martyrs wear justifiable anger best. Being a martyr is a fulltime job and requires years of development and reprogramming. If you are training to become a martyr or if you have already established your martyr status within your family unit, I highly suggest running for political office.

There are more causes to be fought for than there are martyrs to do the fighting. Focus your anger on a cause that honors your spirit. World hunger is one example of what I consider an issue to be justifiably angry about. Children being exploited, men and women suffering physical abuse and war among nations across the globe. These are worthy causes to focus your anger.

I am not amused by justifiable anger at the world for being

unfair. Life is not fair. The world does not owe you fairness
because of your size. There are as many shallow overweight people
as there are kind and caring thin people. Let it go. Let the anger
subside.

How many times have you heard an overweight individual
say: " I would never be attracted to another fat person!" I said it.
I meant it. The thought of someone else reflecting my own body
image frightened me. Denial is difficult to sleep with.

I found redemption in the realization that I was the shallow
human being. I was the one with the problem. And I was the only
one I had the power to change. Get off your high horse. Thin
people aren't hurting us anymore than we are hurting others like us.
Love begins within. If you're finding that you can't find love from
outside sources, I recommend beginning from the inside and
working your way out. We have a talent for using our weight to
keep our bodies from ever connecting with our emotions.
Disconnected, disillusioned and depressed. Denial has never been
so obvious. Obesity is not a mystery. We love to say that our fat
protects us from outsiders. I am saying that our fat numbs us to
getting to know ourselves.

We are whining about how thin people mistreat us. Rarely,
have I heard anyone whine about the poor treatment we give
ourselves. We ignore our feelings, we seek out what we need to fill
inside, we run and we complain. We are sad and we are hurt. And
we are justified. Life is unfair. Overweight martyrs or overweight

victims of cultural expectations, either way we are no lighter. We still can't fit inside a tub or walk up a flight of stairs.

Fair is what we make of it. Let go of your anger, set aside the armor and lift up your spirit. Walk away from your victim stance and race towards the life that you visualize for yourself. Be happy. Be strong. Find health and love from the one source you've never sought out before -Yourself. Stop. Reflect. Accept that you have the power and the responsibility to change your thinking.

Reprogram your mind to love yourself. Reprogram your mind to be honest and true to your own purpose. Teach by example and let go of the martyr mentality.

I am an overweight human being. I grew up fat all my life. I know what it's like to be an overweight teenager. I know the pain of being hurt and ignored. I know how my reactions became my actions. I know that I developed habits to protect myself from further abuse. I know what it means to finally fit comfortably inside my own bathtub, while tears of joy pour down my cheeks. I know what it's like to hear others criticize you when you simply want to eat in peace. I have cried my share of tears.

Today, I look back on who I was and who I've become. I am constantly working towards a better me. A stronger, kinder and more empathetic me. I am learning to love me for who I am and to let go of the many layers of fat that I've built in my mind along with my body. It is a continuous journey to connect your mind and your

body. It is the most rewarding and challenging experience of my
existence.

TIME TO THINK

Take A Moment and answer these questions.

Do you like to do the things you believe you "have to," "should" or "ought to" do?

Are you afraid to trust your instincts? If so, why?

When you say, "you really want," to binge-eat what exactly do you mean?

Do you always need reasons before you allow yourself to binge-eat? If so, why?

Are you afraid if you were just "hungry," it would not be comfortable? If so, what do you believe about being hungry and uncomfortable?

Are you uncertain about what you want and what you need to feel fulfilled?

Are you unclear about what you want and what you need when you are happy?

By, Teri Kai Holtzclaw, Ph.D.   **100**

Points to consider:

Many of us "want" to binge-eat and then, only, do we find reasons
to support our wants.

Reasons do not support our wants.   Reasons simply clarify our
doubts.

We make a choice to give in to our wants or to confront our
reasons.

Ultimately, we all want to align our wants with our needs and do
away with our reasons altogether.

There is no good reason to want to binge-eat. Only good excuses.

 Thank goodness we do not need a reason or an excuse to be
happy.

Ideas you may want to rethink:

Wanting to eat is bad if we have no reasons for it.

There must be something wrong with me.

I don't understand.

Being me is a bad place to be.

If I trusted myself I would only disappoint myself.

THE MAGIC PILL A Mental Health Companion for the Gastric Bypass Patient

An Exercise in Understanding Your Eating Habits

Take a moment and ask yourself the following questions:

- Do you often skip meals?

- Do find yourself drinking more diet beverages than water?

- Are you avoiding foods such as dairy products or protein products to save calories?

- Do you talk about food as being a "bad" or "good" thing?

- Do you either binge or starve yourself?

- Do you snack all the time or never?

- How much time and energy do you spend each day thinking about your weight and specific food concerns?

- Do you judge others by their size and body shape?

- Do you think that being "thinner" will make you happier?

By, Teri Kai Holtzclaw, Ph.D.   **103**

Once you have answered these questions you'll be better equipped
to assess your attitude and views about food. Positive change
occurs when we attempt to alter perceptions that may be negatively
affecting others and ourselves.

Consider for a moment where society is leading your thoughts. The
obsession with being an "ideal" weight is of higher priority than
other areas of life. This imbalance creates chaos throughout our
entire being. It is imperative that we honor all aspects of our
existence and give equal attention to our body mind and spirit.

CONCLUSION

The subject of weight loss maintenance after surgery is a complex topic, affecting the dimensions of physiology, behavior, relationships, mood and thought processes. In my books, I describe some of the affects that these dimensions have and explore the fact that each person experiences weight loss maintenance after surgery somewhat differently.

I'd like to emphasize that mental health approaches need to be as multi-dimensional as the issue is itself. Throughout my practice I am constantly challenged to reinvent new methods to address each unique client I encounter. There is no one sure-fire method or approach that fits all of us.

Finally, any intervention, such as gastric bypass surgery that focuses on only one aspect of weight loss will necessarily be incomplete.

THE MAGIC PILL A Mental Health Companion for the Gastric Bypass Patient

By, Teri Kai Holtzclaw, Ph.D.

About The Author

Five years ago Dr. Holtzclaw underwent gastric bypass surgery and lost over 150 pounds. Today, she is running a thriving practice serving clients who want help from a professional who knows what they are going through. The author of a workbook series called Obtaining/Maintaining Successful Weight Loss for the Bariatric Client, Teri Kai Holtzclaw has also written for numerous publications on issues surrounding mental health and obesity. Teri is a member of the American Society for Bariatric Surgery, The International Federation for the Surgery of Obesity, American Obesity Association and is affiliated with several obesity advocacy groups. When Dr. Holtzclaw is not in session, she speaks to weight loss support groups throughout the southeast and professionals who are interested in working with Bariatric clients.

A world traveler by passion, Teri has lived and visited such exotic places as Thailand, Japan, Russia, Mongolia and China. Teri lives in Atlanta, Georgia with her partner Sandy, and their two children Cleo (cat) and Harley (dog).